Every time you see a heart
know how much I love you!
- Grandma

www.mascotbooks.com

Grandma Hearts™: Bedtime

For more information, please contact:
Mascot Books
560 Herndon Parkway #120
Herndon, VA 20170
info@mascotbooks.com

Library of Congress Control Number: 2016917549

CPSIA Code: PRT0117A
ISBN-13: 978-1-63177-878-0

Printed in the United States

Grandma ♥ Hearts™

Bedtime

by Dionne Kelm

illustrated by Mary Manning

Find the Grandma Hearts

hidden on every page!

It is my sincere belief that every child is entitled to LOVE, JOY, CARE, & KINDNESS!

If you are lucky enough to have a little one in your life, give them an extra kiss tonight from me.

Forever,
Grandma Dionne

My grandma always reads to me
when I am ready for bed.
My grandma reads me lots of books but
"First things first," she says...

First, let me tell you,
oh, how I love you.
Come here my little sweetie pie
and snuggle close to me.

Let me see your clean hands
and your just washed face.
Let me see your shiny teeth,
your toothbrush back in place.

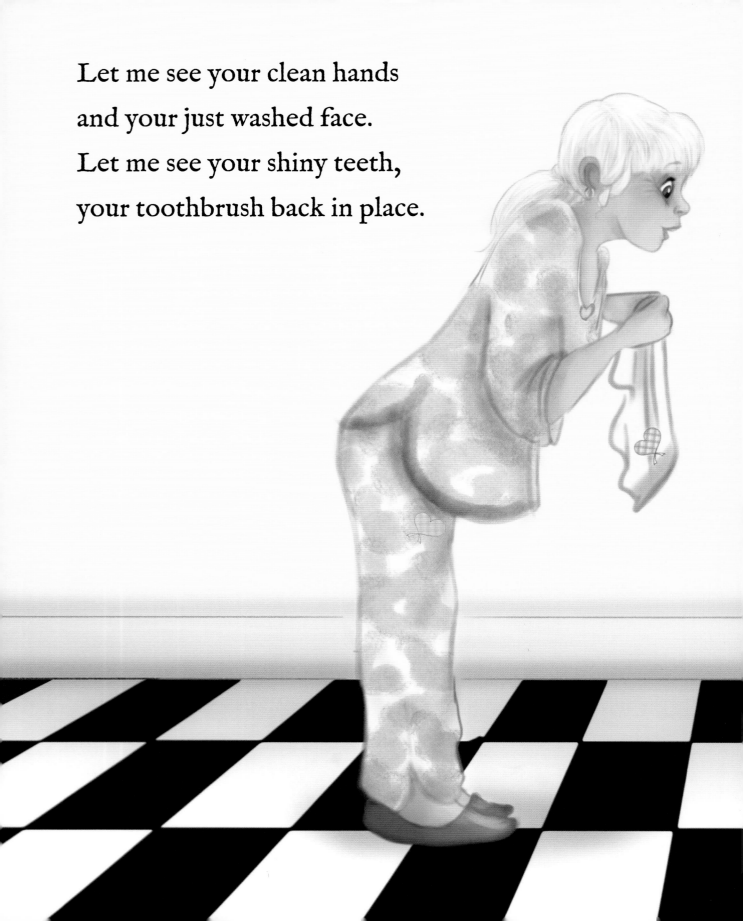

We've picked up all your books and toys.

You know we really should.

We've put away the crayons and building blocks.

A tidy house is good.

You are an awesome gift to me,
as a rainbow to the sky.
I just love to spend my time with you,
as the days go by and by.

When first I knew you'd be here,
you were tiny like a jelly bean.
You hadn't said a single word
and hadn't yet been seen.

Your mommy kept you safe
and sound right below her heart.
You were such happy news for me.
I loved you from the start.

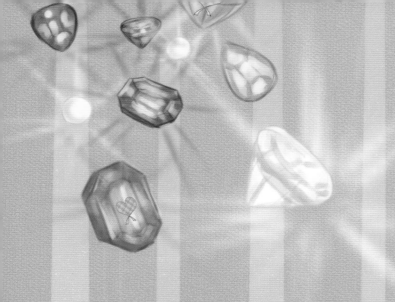

And I knew that you'd be special.
A gem! A jewel! A prize!
Maybe you'd have your daddy's nose
or your mommy's pretty eyes.

And now you're here,
and I am too.
We'll have such fun,
just me and you.

I'll read you books
and songs we'll sing.
We'll take fun walks,
swing on a swing.

We'll play some tag, some Simon Says,
or kick a rolling ball.
Climb way up to the top of the slide.
I'll catch you if you fall!

There are so many things to do
in this fine world, you'll see.
I always love spending time with you.
You're delightful company!

But right now it is your bedtime,
that special time of day.
My story will be ending.
I don't have much more to say.

Except a promise is a promise,
this one I'll always keep.
I'll love you for forever.
Now close your eyes and sleep.

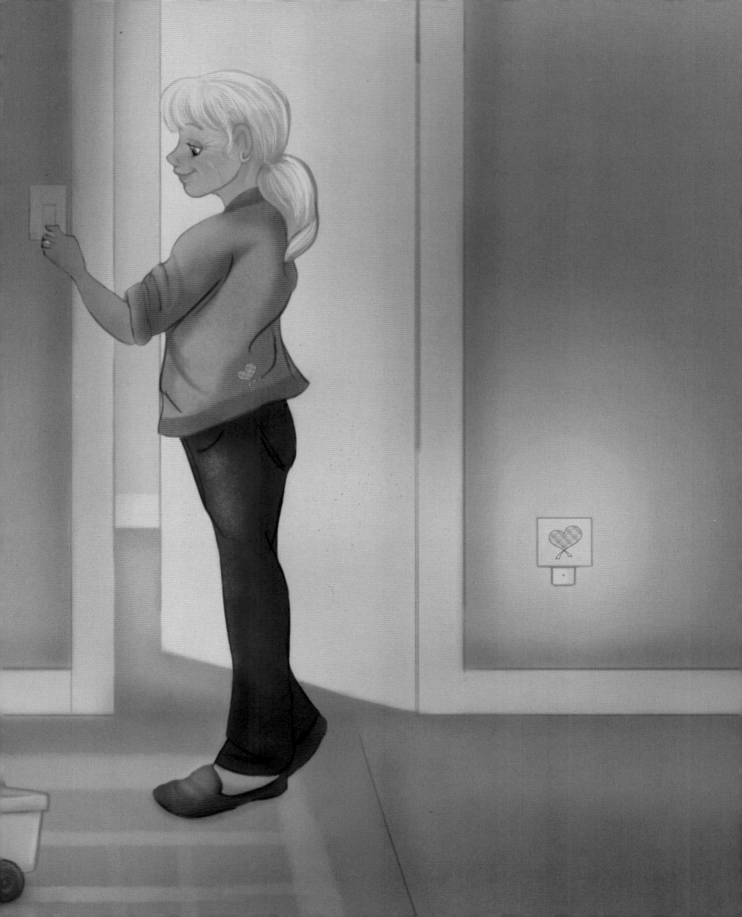

Sweet dreams, I love you.

Goodnight.

Grandma Hearts Bedtime Song

This is the way we get rea-dy for bed.

Wash your face, brush your teeth, lay down your head.

Read you some stor - ies to dream on all night.

Sweet grand child of mine till you wake with dawn's light.

About the Author

Grandma Dionne lives with Grandpa Pete in Watertown, Wisconsin, where they raised their three children, Chase, Adam, and Ivy. She received her "Grandma Heart" the moment she knew she'd be one, when Connor was tiny, like a jelly bean! Since then, she and Grandpa Pete have been blessed with Evelyn, Piper, and New Baby Kelm (debut November 2016).

Grandma Dionne has always had a great love for children and truly believes every child is entitled to LOVE, JOY, CARE, & KINDNESS! Together, with other grandmas, Grandma Dionne hopes to work to make our world the best it can be for our children and grandchildren.